MAKING HISTORY
HOW TO CREATE A HISTORICAL DOCUMENTARY

**The History Channel
for National History Day**

Another title in the NHD
"Making History: How To" series.

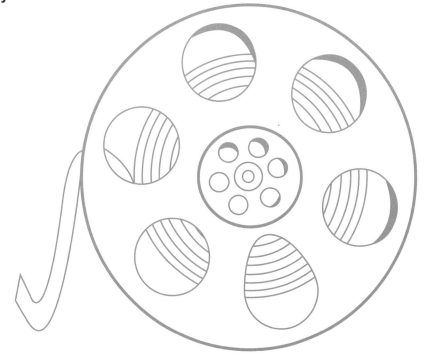

THE HISTORY CHANNEL.
WHERE THE PAST COMES ALIVE.

NHD
NATIONAL
HISTORY DAY

Dear Teachers, Parents, and Students,

On behalf of National History Day (NHD), I am pleased to introduce Making History, a series of instructional materials designed to improve student research and presentation of historical projects through their involvement in the National History Day program.

The Making History series is composed of A Guide to Historical Research for teachers, and a set of four student-focused guidebooks, each designed to direct students in producing creative historical presentations, through exhibits, documentaries, performances, or traditional research papers. NHD collaborated with four nationally recognized organizations who shared their expertise in the following:

How to Create a Historical Exhibit

Developed by the National Archives and Records Administration, this piece guides students through the process of exhibit design, using the same criteria as the professional museum designer utilizes in creating a museum exhibit. Examples of professional exhibits and award-winning NHD student exhibits are included.

How to Create a Historical Documentary

In a guide and accompanying DVD, The History Channel takes students through the process of documentary production and includes tips on storyboarding, credits, and visual impact.

How to Create a Historical Performance

In this guide and DVD, experts at The Colonial Williamsburg Foundation highlight the key areas to consider in developing a historical performance, including tips on script writing, choosing props and costumes, and character development. Sample award-winning NHD performances are included on the DVD.

How to Create a Historical Paper

Our friends at Newsweek Education Program outline the process that takes students from research through the writing process and explain the most effective way to write a coherent, organized, and interesting historical essay.

I am indebted to our partners for sharing their expertise, and to the Winter Group for the series' beautiful design. My special thanks to ABC-CLIO for providing expert editorial and production assistance.

I hope you find the clarity of the content to be user friendly and the authorship to be unrivaled.

Cathy Gorn
Executive Director
National History Day
March 2006

National History Day

For more information about NHD, go to www.nhd.org

For more information about our partners and to discover more about their own educational offerings, visit:

www.historychannel.com	www.nara.gov	www.history.org
www.newsweekeducation.com	www.abc-clio.com	

Library of Congress Cataloging-in-Publication Data

Making history : how to create a historical documentary / the History Channel.
    p. cm.
  "NHD 'making history how-to' series."
  ISBN 1-59884-061-4 (workbook : alk. paper) 1. Documentary films--Production and direction. 2. Historical films. I. National History Day (Organization) II. History Channel (Television network)
  PN1995.9.D6M328 2006
  070.1'8--dc22
                 2006013167

CONTENTS

INTRODUCTION

STUDENTS

Congratulations! You are on your way to producing your own historical documentary. At The History Channel® (THC), we are in the permanent business of making historical documentaries and have put a few of our pointers together for you in the DVD *How to Create a Historical Documentary* and this companion study guide. These were especially made for National History Day (NHD) documentary category participants. If you are entering your documentary in the NHD competition, be sure to follow the criteria in the contest rule book provided by NHD and read the *What are the steps to create a project?* guide on the NHD website http://www.nhd.org/CreatingaProject.htm.

Through viewing this guide, you will learn the overall steps for creating and producing a historical documentary. You will also think critically about how documentaries convey historical information. To get the most out of this study guide, you should read through all of it, answer questions, and complete the activities throughout its pages. This study guide is yours to keep. Three-hole punch it and keep it in a notebook. Write in it, use it to brainstorm, learn from it, and, most of all, have a blast creating your documentary!

EDUCATORS

This study guide and the *How to Create a Historical Documentary* DVD are also useful for teachers who want to provide an introduction to their students interested in creating documentaries. *How to Create a Historical Documentary* is also appropriate for classes focusing on practical techniques of historical interpretation in film and media literacy.

NATIONAL HISTORY DAY

You've decided to participate in NHD. Congratulations! NHD is a great opportunity for students to explore the past while having fun researching, writing, and presenting information about history. There are several NHD contest categories from which to choose. This publication is for those of you who are thinking about creating a documentary as your NHD project.

Making a documentary will give you a chance to use audiovisual equipment.

WHAT IS A DOCUMENTARY?

A documentary should reflect your ability to use audiovisual equipment to communicate your topic's significance, much as professional documentaries on THC do. The documentary category will help you develop skills in using photographs, film, videotapes, audiotapes, computers, and graphic presentations. NHD documentaries present information about an event, person, place, or idea from the past through a ten-minute presentation, typically a video or DVD that showcases documents, images, photographs, and actual footage of the topic you are researching. Your documentary needs to have both primary and secondary research but must also be an original production.

WHY SHOULD I CONSIDER DOING A DOCUMENTARY FOR NHD?

Creating a documentary offers you many chances to work with technology that the other categories do not. Whether you create your documentary using sophisticated computer software or easy-to-use software like Apple's iMovie, you will learn new skills because of the nature of the category. You should also consider if you have an interest in learning these skills because they will be important to you in doing well with this category.

HOW ARE DOCUMENTARIES DIFFERENT FROM OTHER NHD CATEGORIES?

Creating a documentary is different from the other NHD categories. Before you decide to do this category, you should ask yourself the following questions:

1. Am I interested in using computers, cameras, and various other technologies?

2. Can I conduct and record interviews (for the purpose of including film clips in the documentary) for my topic?

3. Can I find film clips to use in my documentary?

4. Are there enough still photographs related to my topic and that I can use in my documentary? (Although no set number of photographs is needed, remember that you want to fill the entire ten minutes with material.)

5. Do I have access to equipment that will be needed to make a documentary (such as computers with video-editing programs such as iMovie, cameras, scanners, and recording devices)?

6. Is creating a documentary the best way to show off my topic? Why or why not? When you have answered these questions, it should be apparent why you should or should not do a documentary. If you feel that you have good access to technology, people you can go to for help, and a desire to create a documentary, then this is the category for you. Keep in mind that not all topics will work well for the documentary category. If, for example, you pick a topic that has very little video or few photographs, then this is not a good category for you to use for the topic you selected. You can either change topics, or change categories if this is the case.

Some aspects of creating a documentary *are* different from other categories:

• Documentaries are typically original film productions.

• Documentaries use live video (if available for your topic), photographs, live interviews, graphics (documents, maps, and so on), as well as words crafted into a script to tell your story.

• Your documentary script should be kept to what is essential for someone to understand your story. You only have ten minutes to do this.

• Documentaries are presented so that everyone can look at (and admire!) your work.

WHAT IS HISTORY?

All NHD projects involve learning about history, but often students are confused about just what "history" means.

History is more than what happened in the past. It is the *record* of past events and it is what historians *write and present* about the past. NHD lets you become a historian and do what historians do. But "doing history" means more than just finding documents and learning facts, it's a way of thinking and a set of skills.

Maybe you think history is just memorizing dates or reading dry textbooks or encyclopedia articles. Or maybe you think history is dull because it happened a long time ago and isn't important to those of us living today. But history is much more exciting than that. Studying history tries to answer the question, "How did we get here?" It gets us to think about how past events shaped the present. Just as an individual needs to understand his or her family's past, its relationships, its problems, and its achievements, it is important for all of us to understand how societies began and changed and how people coped with the challenges of their time. Studying history lets you step out of your time, social background, and place, and examine how life was different than today, and begin to understand people who are not like you. It gets you to think about what people believed and why they made choices they did. Studying history exposes you to many human emotions: the lives of great men and women inspire us, accounts of injustices prompt us to anger; and stories of social and technological invention astonish us. Finally, history teaches important skills such as reading carefully, collecting and evaluating evidence, drawing appropriate conclusions, thinking critically, and writing clearly.

The following list describes some of the skills and tools historians use and why you will need to use them in your project.

- *Tell a story.* To "do history," you have to tell a story. Your story will have a beginning, middle, and an end, and like a spellbinding novel, it will hold the reader's interest. A skilled historian highlights some events as more important than others, and he or she picks out and writes about

dramatic incidents using colorful quotations, vivid images, and facts that bring the past alive. A documentary may not use as many words as a book, but it, too, needs to tell a story. You might choose to organize your documentary chronologically or thematically, but your organization plan should help you to tell your story more clearly.

- *Reveal change over time.* It is easy to point out examples of changes in recent history. Teenagers no longer listen to their favorite bands on 45-rpm records; they download music from the Internet. Many more women work outside the home today than did so fifty years ago. For more than a generation, the Democratic party usually had most of the seats in the U.S. House of Representatives. In 1994, the Republican party won control of the House. Historians are fascinated with change. They try to figure out not only how things changed (or didn't change), but why. As you work on your NHD documentary, don't just ask what happened, but what led to an event, and why it happened at a specific moment in time?

- *Consider historical perspective.* Think about what you would tell someone about a day in the life of your school. You would probably describe what you did during the day, and maybe you would report on your friends' activities, but wouldn't you also want to include what your principal did? What about your teachers, the librarian, and the custodial staff? Wouldn't you want to include their stories, and get their perspectives, too, so you could make a complete picture of the day as possible?

When you investigate a historical event, it is also important to look for and understand the

different points of view of its participants—to look for different *historical perspectives*. For example, June 6, 1944—the day the Allies invaded Nazi-held Northern Europe—meant very different things depending on who and where you were. An Allied infantryman on Omaha beach had a very different perspective on that day than did General Dwight D. Eisenhower, who was in England. A French Resistance fighter had a different experience from a German soldier, or from an American woman working in an aircraft factory in California. A good historian considers these perspectives and weaves them into his or her story. A good documentary includes documents, photos, and interviews if applicable, that consider multiple perspectives.

- *Provide context.* Our lives are greatly influenced by when and where we live. People who lived in the past were no different. A French peasant who lived in 1760 had only a few options about where he could live or work. A woman living in England in 1850 could not run for political office or even vote. Likewise, the places where we lived shaped how individuals and societies developed. The fact that Pope John Paul II was born in Poland profoundly affected the rest of his life. Communities and social institutions developed very differently in the dry American West than along New England's seashores. Historians refer to an understanding of

how time and place affect history as having an appreciation of *context*. A superior NHD documentary will illustrate how time and place influenced events. This can be done in a number of ways. A timeline might note what other events happened at the same time as your topic. A letter or page of a memoir displayed might describe how a person's hometown affected his or her outlook. A photo or artwork could be used to create an environment that reminds the viewer of the time and place a person lived. Along with your documentary's script, the placement of photos, video footage, and music all play an important role in creating the passage you want your viewers to understand.

One technique that may help you to think about geographical context of an event is to ask "why there?" To think about how a time may have influenced an event ask, "why then?"[1]

- *Ask questions.* The stories a historian or curator tells have a lot to do with the questions he or she asks about the past. Good questions come from a thorough understanding of your topic and the research you do. Sometimes these questions can't be answered by a simple yes or no. Instead, they will lead you to more questions. Important questions about the past result from thinking critically about your topic. Critical thinking does not mean disapproving or fault finding. It means analyzing what is important. Here are a two examples of different types of historical questions—one easy and one more complex.

    1. Thomas Jefferson wrote the Declaration of Independence. Did he also own slaves? *Yes. This is a simple yes or no question. It is based entirely on facts. Little discussion will flow from this question.*

2. Thomas Jefferson wrote the Declaration of Independence. He was also a slave owner. How did he reconcile his belief, "all men are created equal," with the fact that he was a slave owner? This is a much more complicated (and interesting!) question. To try to answer it, you need to know something about Jefferson's life and thought as well as the time in which he was living. This question also leads to many others. For example, how did Jefferson and men like him understand the meaning of the word "freedom?" What did Jefferson think about the question of equality between European and African Americans? Did Jefferson think there were any alternatives except slavery and complete freedom for all slaves? Questions like these will also lead you to a variety of historical sources such as biographies of Jefferson, his writings, and historical documents from the time.

- *Draw conclusions.* A good historian does more than just describe how events happened. He or she draws conclusions about the past. Your documentary needs to do this, too. Ideally, your conclusions will closely relate to the NHD theme. For example, if the NHD theme is *The Individual in History*, a documentary about Martin Luther King's philosophy of nonviolence might conclude that King's reading of Mahatma Gandhi was a key to the tactics he used in the civil rights movement. If the NHD theme is *Frontiers in History*, your documentary on the space race could emphasize Cold War hostility and fear between the United States and Union of Soviet Socialist Republics (USSR) as the most important factor in the contest to get to the Moon. As long as your conclusions are based on solid evidence, don't be afraid of having a point of view.

- *Find facts, facts, and more facts.* History is more than facts and dates, but that doesn't mean facts and dates aren't important to a historian. To tell a story, describe a time and place, ask questions of the past, and draw conclusions, you have to get your facts right. Being able to answer "who," "what," "when," and "where," about your topic will equip you to take on these more challenging tasks. Think of facts and dates as the foundation of a house you are constructing. Getting your facts right builds a solid foundation; inaccuracies will make the house fall down.

CHOOSING YOUR DOCUMENTARY TOPIC

One of your first big decisions is to pick a topic for your NHD project. There is no one way to come up with a great topic. It might come from reading a book, from a discussion with a teacher, or even watching a film on TV. The following steps describe ways that might help you to choose one that will work well for a documentary.

- *Brainstorm topics that relate to the year's NHD theme.* History Day themes change each year. This year's theme may be *The Individual in History*. Next year's might be *Triumph and Tragedy in History*. Your topic needs to focus on the year's theme. For example, if the theme is *Communication in History,* you might consider topics such as how Lewis Hine's photographs of child labor in the United States

The National History Day theme for 2003 was Rights and Responsibilities

The National History Day theme for 2004 was Exploration, Encounter, Exchange

The National History Day theme for 2005 was Communication in History

raised public awareness of the practice, or the importance of propaganda in Nazi Germany. If the theme is *Rights and Responsibilities in History*, you might want to cover a topic such as why some Japanese Americans joined the armed forces during World War II while others resisted the draft and went to prison instead. Remember, *relation to the theme* counts for 20 percent of the score you receive from the contest judges, so look for a topic that will match the theme closely.

- *Determine what historical resources are nearby.* You don't have to travel to China to do your research on building the Great Wall, and you don't have to go to Warsaw to study the Solidarity labor movement. Primary research materials come from local libraries, from the Internet, and from interviews with participants who live near you. If you have a passionate interest in such a topic, go for it! Your enthusiasm and research can make up for your lack of nearby sources.

However, there are advantages to choosing a topic where a number of your primary sources are close. A local historical society may have diaries or letters from participants in a historical event. An archive may have photographs, film, or sound recordings that relate to your topic. Newspaper accounts may be available on microfilm at a nearby library.

- *Think through controversial topics.* Was President Truman justified in ordering American airmen to drop the first atomic bomb on Japan? What limitations have governments put on free speech during wartime? Did the 1917 revolution improve the lives of the Russian people? Historians and documentary filmmakers deal with controversial subjects all the time. Lively debates among historians about touchy topics are part of what makes history so fascinating, and there are many thoughtful points of view on most historical subjects. If you are thinking about tackling a controversial historical issue, be sure to first get your parents' or guardian's and your teacher's approval. Of course, your topic will need to relate to the NHD theme. Most importantly, your NHD project needs to deal with the topic in *history*. If, for example, you are going to do a documentary about the second Amendment to the Constitution, which guarantees "the right to bear arms," remember that your exhibit should focus on the history of the amendment. It is *not* an opportunity to give your opinions on current day gun control controversies.

Just as important as following the NHD theme is selecting a topic that you find interesting. You are going to be working on your project for several months. Picking a topic that interests you will make that time much more enjoyable.

CONDUCTING HISTORICAL RESEARCH

- *Do your secondary research first.* You've chosen a great topic. Your teacher has approved it, and you can't wait to visit a local archive, do an interview with someone who participated in your historical event, or read old newspaper stories about it.

Stop!

Every historian looks forward to doing research in *primary sources*. If you are excited about history, it's only natural to want to read a letter from the eighteenth century, listen to an early sound recording, or hold an old map in your hands. But before you start looking for those primary sources, you need to prepare by first reading *secondary sources*—books and journal articles written by historians on your topic, talking with experts, and visiting trustworthy websites that will give you accurate information. These steps will help you understand your subject more completely, point you toward primary sources, and assist you in deciding what important themes you want to investigate and the key questions you want to ask.

- *The possibilities and problems of Web research.* The World Wide Web has made conducting historical research much easier and placed huge numbers of historical documents at your fingertips. Many reputable universities, libraries, museums, archives, government agencies, and other organizations have excellent and accurate websites that you can rely on. However, don't try to do all your research on the Web. Information on the Web tends to

Study secondary sources first to learn about your NHD topic.

simplify complicated issues. Remember too, that *anyone* with a little skill with website design can put *anything* on a site, no matter how inaccurate. Some sites are also associated with groups that have political, religious, or other motives. These groups may choose to cite "facts" that agree with them and not mention those that don't fit the cause they are promoting.

NHD has created an excellent website about evaluating Internet sites. For this and other research tips, go to http://www.nhd.org/ResearchSources.htm.

- *The exciting world of primary sources.* NHD defines a *primary source* as "materials directly related to a topic by time or participation." These primary sources might take the form of letters or diaries, manuscript collections, photographs, drawings, and other works of art, songs, maps, government records, newspapers, magazines, oral history interviews, or artifacts.

Sorting out primary from secondary sources can be complicated. The key to spotting a primary source is watching for phrases indicating time or participation. For example, a newspaper article from 1878 describing that year's Paris International Exposition is a primary source. If the article was written by a journalist who visited the Exposition or an architect who designed one of the buildings, it is also connected to the event through participation. An article or book about the Exposition written in 2001 by a historian is a secondary source.

Other types of primary sources need to be evaluated by using the same test. A taped interview with a historian about prisoners of war during World War II is a secondary source unless that historian happened to be a prisoner or somehow else participated—for example, if he was a soldier who helped to liberate the prison. A song sung by British troops in the trenches during World War I is a primary source. A song written by a songwriter looking back on the war from today is a secondary source.

It is possible for the same source to be both primary and secondary, depending on how it is being used. A history textbook is usually a secondary source, but what if you were doing a documentary about how American history textbooks in the 1950s viewed American history? Then, a textbook published in 1954 would become a primary source.

Now that you understand the definition of primary sources, how do you find them? A good first step

Visit museums and archives to view primary sources.

is to look at the secondary source books and articles you read. They will often have footnotes and bibliographies that refer you to manuscript collections, oral histories, photography holdings, and other sources. Another approach is to talk with your librarian and teacher and get their suggestions. Or, you might want to contact a professor at a university who specializes in your subject area, and ask him or her what primary sources are available for your subject.

The NHD website http://www.nhd.org/Research Roadmap.htm has *A Research Roadmap* with much more information about understanding and using primary sources.

• *Evaluate your evidence.* Just because a source was created at the time of the event you are studying or by a participant in that event doesn't mean it's true or important. The primary sources you display are evidence that needs to be evaluated, analyzed, and interpreted. This process will allow you to judge how valuable each source is to the story you are telling and to the points you are trying to make. Here are some important questions to ask about any source.[2]

   1. *What type of source is this?* Evaluating different types of sources calls for different sets of skills and raises different questions. A letter may be able to be read easily for the information it contains. (Unless it is in a foreign language!) "Reading" a poster requires knowledge of the life of the artist, the techniques he or she used to create it, the symbolism it contains, and its intended audience. Knowing something about the type of source also will help you to think about the past in different ways. A photograph of the civil rights march in Selma, Alabama,

may raise a different set of questions for you than a written description of the march does.

2. *What is the date of the source?* Dating a document allows you to put it into historical perspective—to place it in time. A petition about the U.S. military draft written just before World War II will have a very different historical context than one written during the Vietnam War. A date can also tell you something about the reliability of the source. A diary entry from the day an event happened is often much more reliable than a memoir written 50 years later, even if both were written by the same participant.

3. *Who created this source?* If you know who created a primary source, you can learn something about why it was created and for what purpose. Newspaper accounts are usually factual, but may be biased by the political views of the paper. A letter written by someone involved in a scandal may try to justify his or her actions. A photograph of children working in a coalmine may have been taken by someone who wants to pass legislation to end child labor. You may be able to tell something about the creator's motivation.

4. *Where was the source produced?* This question raises issues of historical context. Two sources documenting the same event that were created in two different places may have dramatically dissimilar views of that event. A newspaper account of the Confederate attack on Fort Sumter in 1861 written in Boston, Massachusetts, would be quite different from one written in Charleston, South Carolina.

- Primary sources are "the raw stuff of history,"[3] and they will be an important part of your documentary research. However, don't forget that to get the most out of your sources, you need to have a thorough knowledge of your topic based on your reading in secondary sources. As you study your primary sources, reread some of the secondary accounts again. You may find you have new insights or realize you have new questions to ask.

CHAPTER REFERENCES

1. Jim Schmidt, "Writing Historical Essays: An Introduction" http://www.niu.edu/history/manual.htm

2. This list is based on Document Analysis Worksheets created by the National Archives and Records Administration's education staff: http://www.archives.gov/education/lessons/worksheets/ and on Kathryn Walbert, "Reading Primary Sources: An Introduction for Students," http://www.learnnc.org/students/9-12/research/print/readingprimaryintro

3. Stacey Bredhoff, *American Originals* (Washington, DC: National Archives and Records Administration in association with the University of Washington Press), 2001, 6.

WORDS TO KNOW

Context

The background, time, or environment that shapes a historical event or the life of an individual.

Narrative

An account of a historical event or the biography of an individual structured in such a way that it tells a story. A narrative can be done in chronological order or by thematic organization, but usually has a strong sense of sequential order.

Historical perspective

An individual's point of view on a historic event, movement, or person. The "place" from which an individual views that event or person. This includes not only geographic location (for example, looking at a battle from a hill above the fight or on the battlefield) or individual outlook (a father may have a different perspective than his daughter about her date), but also intellectual, political, economic, social, religious, or other perspectives. (For example, the different perspectives of worker and a manager on a strike, or of a liberal Democrat from a conservative Republican on a bill in Congress.)

Primary source

Historical materials directly related to a topic by time or participation. These may take the form of an original diary entry, an oral history, a historical photograph, or a petition.

Secondary source

Historical materials on a topic not related by time or participation. For example, books and articles by historians or interviews with professors are usually secondary sources.

GETTING STARTED: TO BE SOLO, OR NOT TO BE?

At The History Channel (THC), we work as a team to produce our documentaries, but for National History Day (NHD), you can work either solo or in a group. You should determine the pros and cons of going either route and make the best decision for yourself. A good resource to help you figure out what works best for you is the *Working in Groups* worksheet contract and questionnaire on the NHD website http://www.nhd.org/CreatingaProject.htm.

Would you prefer to work on your NHD documentary alone, with a partner, or with a group?

GENERAL MATERIALS NEEDED FOR YOUR PROJECT

1. *Documentary Notebook* to write down all of your ideas and keep your research organized

2. *Access to*

   a. A *computer* to type up your script

   b. A *video camera* (preferably, digital) to shoot your documentary

   c. *Editing software* such as iMovie or Final Cut Pro

   d. *Supplies*: batteries (make sure recharge-able batteries are fully charged), blank DVDs or videotapes, paper, pens, props

3. The *passion* to discover and tell a dynamite story from history

MATERIALS NEEDED FOR THIS STUDY GUIDE

1. The *How to Create a Historical Documentary* DVD

2. Pen or pencil to answer questions in the study guide

3. Additional materials as listed for each activity in Part III: Skill-Strengthening

RESOURCE TIP

For an in-depth, step-by-step guide for creating an NHD documentary with Apple's iMovie, you can buy a copy of *The Past in Pixels: Using iMovie to Create a NHD Documentary* from the NHD national office. Go to the NHD website http://www.nhd.org/shop.htm, NHD Materials, link to the order form.

PART I: BEFORE POPPING IN THE DVD

Before viewing *How to Create a Historical Documentary*, write your answers to the following questions. If you are on a team, also be sure to discuss your responses together.

1. How do you define a historical documentary? Give some examples of documentaries you consider to be historical documentaries and why.

_____

_____

_____

_____

2. How does a historical documentary differ from a historical drama (such as *Gladiator, Windtalkers, Amistad, The Patriot*)?

_____

_____

_____

_____

3. In your opinion, what makes a good historical documentary? Give some examples of documentaries you think are really good, and explain why you think they are good.

_____

_____

_____

_____

4. How does presenting an argument (thesis) in a documentary differ from doing so in a paper or a book? How is it similar?

_____

_____

_____

_____

PART II: REEL TALK

VIEWING GUIDE

Instructions

After you answer the questions in Part I, read through this viewing guide, pop in *How to Create a Historical Documentary,* and complete the missing information in the following material. Feel free to watch the DVD twice or pause and review as often as you need to get the right information!

FOR STARTERS

The top question filmmakers have been asking themselves for a long time is this

How do you best capture _____ and tell a _____ at the same time?

The first step is coming up with a(n) _____.

Then you want to start planning by (1) creating a budget, (2) having a creative vision, and (3) creating a production _____ with deadlines for each task.

Making a documentary basically boils down to three stages

1. Pre-Production—when you _____ and set things up.

2. _____—when you're shooting video and gathering pictures and sound.

3. Post-Production—when you take all your material and put it together in a(n) _____ session.

RESEARCH—THIS IS THE MOST IMPORTANT STEP

Start by looking at secondary sources such as books, magazines, and the Internet. Even though the _____is a treasure trove of information, the facts you find there might not be correct. This is why you'll need to track down _____ sources to back up your findings. Think of it as actual history you can see, hear, or touch.

Keep a list of all of your sources and production information in a binder, whether you use the information or not. The producer in the film says if you're working with a team, create a _____— a notebook, file, or shared computer folder that everyone can access. This is important because you don't want to do the same work twice.

Top Five Things to Keep in Mind During This Phase

- Keep a central database.

- Communicate with your team.

- Stick to your schedule and budget.

- _____ will be an ongoing process throughout production.

- Use _____ sources to back up your findings.

THE SCRIPT

Now that you've started your research, how do you know what to focus on? Think hard about your topic—find your _____, and think of how you can tell this story in your own unique way.

You might want to use interviews or maybe reenactments will help. Think about what _____, sound, pictures, or paintings you'll need.

After you think about all this, you should write a synopsis, which is basically a(n) _____ describing how you plan to tell the story on screen.

When you're writing your script, make sure to double-check your _____ with confirmation from at least two reliable sources.

SHOOT + FOOTAGE

When shooting your interviews, look for a place that's visually interesting and looks good on _____
_____.

If you can't interview someone face to face, remember, you can do a _____ interview instead.

What's the first question you should ask your interviewee?

"Can you state your _____ please, and spell it?"

THE EDIT

The History Channel (THC) producer says,

"Before you walk into your edit session, you need to be fully prepared. You need to make sure you have screened all of your _____ and you know exactly what you want to put into your piece." Keep a list of time codes of each shot so that you can find everything easily in the edit.

"The one thing you have to remember is that a story is a story. The best way to tell a story is through beautiful _____, through beautiful visuals and it's not about the technology, it's not about the money, it's about the _____ that you're putting into your story."

CREDITS

Credits are like _____ in a term paper.

Be sure to acknowledge everyone and all of your _____.

REEL TALK: SPEAKING THE LINGO

After you watch *How to Create a Historical Documentary*, use any of the resources listed at the end of this guide, a dictionary (www.meriamwebster.com), or the Internet to define the following terms. Write your definitions next to each word.

- b-roll

- budget

- copyright

- credits

- database

- fact-checking

- footage

- graphics

- primary sources

- reel

- rough cut

- secondary sources

- storyboard

- synopsis

- time code

- timeline

- voice over

PART III: SKILL STRENGTHENING

PHASE I: PRE-PRODUCTION

Find a topic that interests you and that relates to this years' NHD topic.

ACTIVITY 1: IN SEARCH OF INSPIRATION

CHOOSE A TOPIC

MATERIALS NEEDED (1) BRAIN POWER, (2) A GOOD IDEA, AND (3) WRITING MATERIALS TO DOCUMENT YOUR BRAINSTORMING ACTIVITIES

QUICK TAKE

A good idea can pop up anywhere. As the historian in the program pointed out, one way to choose your topic is to select a commonly known story and then find a different angle that brings something new to it. Remember that there are many unknown stories that also should be told. Regardless of the topic you select, choose one that truly interests you, and remember to put it into historical context.

TRY IT OUT!

- Keeping in mind this year's NHD theme, flip through history textbooks, browse the Internet, talk to family members and teachers, and watch The History Channel (THC) for cool historical topics.

- For the next week, keep a journal of every conversation, idea, and dream you have on topics that interest you.

- At the end of the week, see if any ideas lend themselves to fitting this year's NHD theme.

- Download and complete the NHD *Topic selection worksheet* from the NHD website http://www.nhd.org/CreatingaProject.htm to help you select your topic.

ACTIVITY 2: GET ORGANIZED!

CREATE A DATABASE

MATERIALS NEEDED 3-RING BINDER WITH DIVIDERS OR COMPUTER

QUICK TAKE

As one of our producers said in the video, it is important that you have a database where you keep track of all of the information you are gathering. A *database* is simply any place where you can collect and easily access your sources and production materials. It can take the form of a 3-ring binder with dividers or files in folders on a computer. Choose whatever format works best for you. It is also important if you are working on a team to have this database accessible to everyone so that you won't duplicate any tasks. You should keep at least the following items organized for yourself.

- *Administrative Information* This includes your timeline, budget, and contact information for everyone involved in the production of your project.

- *Research* This includes a list of all the sources you have encountered, a list of interviewees and their contact information, photocopies of your primary sources (for example, letters, pictures, and newspaper articles).

- *Script Ideas* This includes your synopsis, your script ideas, and latest draft of your script.

- *Edit Session Materials* This includes your Footage List (list of time codes from the footage you'd like to use). You'll learn about this in Activity 9.

TRY IT OUT!

- Decide how you want to organize the information you will gather and the work you'll do during this project. Do you want to store all your information on a computer? In a 3-ring binder? In file cabinets? All of the above?

- Gather the necessary materials and begin naming and organizing your folders and sections.

ACTIVITY 3: THE CLOCK IS TICKING

CREATE A TIMELINE

MATERIALS NEEDED (1) A CALENDAR, (2) NHD CONTEST GUIDE FOR DEADLINES, AND (3) PEN AND PAPER

QUICK TAKE

Before you jump into your project, it is a good idea to create a preliminary time-line of when you want to finish important steps along the way, especially the start and end dates of pre-production, research, production, and post-production. You especially want to highlight when you want to finish the following:

1. Rough draft of script

2. Final draft of script

3. Shooting (including your interviews)

4. Rough cut of film

5. Final draft of film

The more detailed your timeline, the better!

BE PREPARED YOU WILL HAVE TO CONTINUOUSLY REVISIT YOUR TIMELINE TO MAKE SURE YOU'RE ON TRACK, BUT ALSO KEEP IN MIND THAT YOU CAN MAKE CHANGES IF YOU NEED TO.

TRY IT OUT!

- Brainstorm and make a list of important tasks that you need to complete throughout your project.

- Using a calendar and keeping in mind NHD deadlines, select the dates by which you want to fulfill each task for your project. Make your timeline as detailed as possible to keep you on track!

- Put your timeline in your database.

ACTIVITY 4: MONEY MATTERS

CREATE A BUDGET

MATERIALS NEEDED (1) PEN AND PAPER OR A COMPUTER, (2) PARENT'S OR GUARDIAN'S APPROVAL, AND (3) CALCULATOR OR BRAIN POWER

QUICK TAKE

On the practical side of things, you also need to have a sense of the costs you may run into while doing this project. Remember: *You don't have to break the bank to make a film.* Spending more money does not make a film better in quality. National History Day (NHD) writes on its website:

The most important aspect of any entry is its historical quality. Students should not get so caught up in the production of a documentary that they lose sight of the importance of the historical quality. Judges are not looking for glitzy productions; rather, they are looking for solid research and a thorough analysis of the chosen topic.

So, think creatively about where you can borrow resources. Does your school have video cameras? Does your neighbor have editing software? Will the local television station allow you to use its facilities? You never know until you ask!

TRY IT OUT!

- Take a look at the *Preparing Your Budget* and *Sample Budget* on the following pages.

- Using the *Budget Worksheet*, create a preliminary budget for your project: Make three copies of the worksheet and do a budget chart for (1) pre-production, (2) production, and (3) post-production. Add the three subtotals to figure out the cost for your entire project. Feel free to add additional items you think you'll need that are not included in the sample.

- When you have completed your preliminary budget, let a teacher or parent review it and help you make any changes for your final budget.

- Be sure to get your parent's or guardian's approval of your final budget.

(continued on next page)

ACTIVITY 4: MONEY MATTERS (cont.)

PREPARING YOUR BUDGET

MATERIALS YOU DEFINITELY NEED

PRE-PRODUCTION	PRODUCTION	POST-PRODUCTION
• Computer/Internet—For research and to write script • 3-ring binder notebook • Dividers • Paper • Phone—To make contact with archives and interviewees • Photocopying (Research)	• Computer/Internet—To edit script • Camcorder (preferably a digital video camera) • Back up battery for camcorder • Tripod • Videotape stock	• Camcorder (preferably a digital video camera) • Computer with editing software • Blank recordable DVDs (DVD+R) or VHS tapes—To show your finished documentary • Music • Stills (visuals such as photographs and paintings) • TV with VCR or DVD

MATERIALS YOU MIGHT NEED

PRE-PRODUCTION	PRODUCTION	POST-PRODUCTION
• Scanner and laptop—To scan photographs and other primary sources at archives if they let you	• Audiotape recorder—to record interviews and use for transcriptions • Audiotapes • Still camera—to take pictures of interviewees and locations so that you remember what they look like	• Sound effects • Graphics/graphic design software

Can you think of anything else?

ACTIVITY 4: MONEY MATTERS (cont.)

SAMPLE BUDGET

TITLE OF PROJECT SLAVE QUILTS: COMMUNICATION IN HISTORY

PHASE PRODUCTION

BUDGET PREPARED BY ANDREW MOORE

Item	Reason	Type (if applicable)	Source	Quantity	Cost per Unit	TOTAL
EQUIPMENT						
Camcorder (video camera)	Shooting	Digital	School	1	FREE	$0
Tripod	Shooting		School	1	FREE	$0
Videotape stock	Shooting	Mini-dv	Store	3 (1 pkg = 3 mini-dv tape)	$16	$48
Batteries	For audiotape recorder and still camera	Double AA	Store	1 pack (4 batteries)	$4	$4
Back-up battery for camcorder (video camera)			School		FREE	$0
Audiotape recorder	To record interviewees and for transcription		Friend			$0
Audiotapes	To record interviewees	90 minute	Store	1 pack (5 tapes)	$5	$5
Still camera	To take a picture of interviewees and locations so that I remember what they look like	Digital (no need for film)	Mom's	1	FREE	$0
SUPPLIES						
Photocopying	Just in case				$10	$10
OTHER						
Travel	None—Staying in hometown				FREE	$0
SUBTOTAL						
						$67

(continued on next page)

BUDGET WORKSHEET

Complete one sheet for each phase of your project. After you have done this, calculate the total costs for your documentary on the next page.

TITLE OF PROJECT_____

PHASE_____

BUDGET PREPARED BY_____

Item	Reason	Type (if applicable)	Source	Quantity	Cost per Unit	TOTAL
EQUIPMENT						
SUPPLIES						
Photocopying						
OTHER						
Phone						
Food						
Travel						
SUBTOTAL						

ACTIVITY 4: MONEY MATTERS (cont.)

CALCULATE TOTAL

PRE-PRODUCTION SUBTOTAL: __________

PRODUCTION SUBTOTAL: __________

POST-PRODUCTION SUBTOTAL: __________

TOTAL __________

Budget Reviewed by

____

Name of Parent/Guardian/Teacher

____

Signature of Parent/Guardian/Teacher

Budget Approved by

____

Name of Parent/Guardian

____

Signature of Parent/Guardian

ACTIVITY 5: RESEARCH

MATERIALS NEEDED (1) ARCHIVES, LIBRARIES, HISTORICAL SOCIETIES—ANY PLACE THAT HAS PRIMARY SOURCES; AND (2) SECONDARY SOURCES

QUICK TAKE

Your research is the most important step for your NHD entry.

Let's say it again:

RESEARCH is the *MOST IMPORTANT* step for your NHD entry

It not only counts as 60 percent of your score, but it is the *foundation of your documentary*. Filmmakers rely on good research to learn and understand the history of their topic. As you encounter sources, you should have this in the back of your mind: *How can this source help me illustrate the story on camera?* You also want to be sure to keep a list of every source you find so that you can find specific photographs, video, and audio when you need it to put together your documentary.

TRY IT OUT!

- Step 1. Your first stop for understanding how you should go about your research should be the A Research Roadmap guide on the National History Day (NHD) website http://www.nhd.org/ResearchRoadmap.htm. Read through *A Research Roadmap* before proceeding with this study guide.

- Step 2. Complete the *Research strategy worksheet* on the NHD website http://www.nhd.org/CreatingaProject.htm (number 5 under *Creating A Project*).

- Put your *Research strategy worksheet* in your folder.

ACTIVITY 6: WHO CAN I TALK TO?

PREPARING FOR THE INTERVIEW

MATERIALS NEEDED (1) COMPUTER TO CREATE A RELEASE FORM AND TRANSCRIBE INTERVIEWS, AND (2) PHONE BOOK OR INTERNET TO FIND THE CONTACT INFORMATION OF A POTENTIAL INTERVIEWEE

QUICK TAKE

During your research, you will run into names of people who were involved in the historical event you are studying or authors who have written about your subject. These people are perfect candidates to be interviewees in your documentary. When you select a person to interview, make sure you do your research beforehand about who he or she is and what you think he or she can contribute to your project. Have the person sign a release form allowing you permission to use his or her interview in your documentary. After you have interviewed a subject, be sure to *transcribe* the interview (type out every word your interviewee says) or at least keep a record of important topics mentioned and note the time code on the tape so that you can find just that portion quickly during the edit session.

TRY IT OUT!

- Take a look at The History Channel (THC) *Guidelines for Oral History Interviews* online at http://www.historychannel.com/classroom/oralhistguidelines.pdf.

- Follow the guide's instructions to make contact with an interviewee and set up an interview time.

- Create a *release form* tailored to your National History Day (NHD) project. You can find a sample release form/permission slip in the THC *Oral History Guidelines*. Let your teacher or parent or guardian review it and make any changes, if needed.

- Make extra copies of your release form and put it in your database.

ACTIVITY 7: WHAT'S YOUR STORY?

WRITE A SYNOPSIS

MATERIALS NEEDED PEN AND PAPER, OR A COMPUTER

QUICK TAKE

So, you have done a lot of research and have a sense of the story you want to tell. Can you tell yours in a paragraph? What about two sentences? Before filmmakers write the script, they write a synopsis (summary) of the story they have discovered. It's like telling the entire story in a couple of sentences or a paragraph, but with language that hints to the style of your documentary.

- Check out examples of synopses on The History Channel (THC) website www.history.com by selecting any nonseries documentary listed in the TV Schedule section.

- Write a synopsis that summarizes what the story is and gives the reader a sense of the style of your project. You can write your synopsis below or type it on a computer.

- When you have completed your synopsis, let a teacher or parent or guardian review it to make sure it is clear.

- Be sure to put your synopsis in your database when you are finished.

BUILDING BLOCKS FOR YOUR SYNOPSIS

On a separate piece of paper, answer these questions first before you tackle writing your synopsis. Write as much as needed to get all of your ideas out.

- What is your story?

- What is your thesis (argument)?

- What evidence did you find that backs it up?

- Why is the story important?

ACTIVITY 7: WHAT'S YOUR STORY? (cont.)

YOUR SYNOPSIS

Using your answers to these questions and thinking about the creative style of your documentary, try writing two versions of your synopsis.

If you had to sum up the story in a paragraph, what is it?

If you had to sum up the story in two sentences, what is it?

ACTIVITY 8: SCRIPT IT!

CREATE A SCRIPT AND STORYBOARD

MATERIALS NEEDED INFORMATION LEARNED FROM YOUR RESEARCH

QUICK TAKE

Now that you have a synopsis, you can begin putting the rough draft of your script together. For documentary filmmakers, we are interested in how to tell a story visually. One way we do this with our preliminary script is to create a storyboard, where we take notes on the images we think will illustrate the audio well.

TRY IT OUT!

• Study the Sample Script on the next page and identify its major features.

• Using a storyboard form from the National History Day (NHD) website http://www.nhd.org/ Documentary.htm, Creating a storyboard, begin storyboarding your script. First, write your narration in the right column. Then write down notes about possible images you want to use to illustrate the story in the far left column. You can also recreate this table on the computer.

• Afterward, go back through the primary sources you have and write in any that might fulfill your vision.

SAMPLE SCRIPT

The **left column** contains the **visual clips** that appear on screen.

The **right column** contains the audio—words spoken by the narrator (voice over), interviewees, and/or sound effects.

HOW TO MAKE A HISTORICAL DOCUMENTARY
4/15/06

OPENING GRAPHICS

CLIP	VO/SFX
GFX: "THE IDEA"	
B-Roll: Quick montage of various historical images from AETN archives—people/places/events to space/lightbulb/building	THERE'S A LOT MORE TO HISTORY THAN PEOPLE, PLACES, AND EVENTS.
B-Roll: New York City	HISTORY IS ALSO ABOUT EXPLORING, INVENTING, AND CREATING.
B-Roll: Various B-roll of Lower Manhattan	SO HOW DO YOU BEST CAPTURE HISTORY AND TELL A STORY AT THE SAME TIME? THAT'S A QUESTION THAT FILMMAKERS, LIKE YOURSELVES, HAVE BEEN ASKING FOR SOME TIME. THE FIRST STEP IS COMING UP WITH AN IDEA! THINK ABOUT WHERE YOU LIVE—AND WHAT RESOURCES YOU HAVE NEARBY.
Video Clip: Producer looking up at Washington Statue at Federal Hall	STRETCH YOUR IMAGINATION . . . AND THEN, THE LIGHTBULB WILL GO ON OVER YOUR HEAD.
Video Clip: Producer & Production Manager go over budget	ONCE THAT HAPPENS, YOU'LL NEED TO START PLANNING AHEAD. THINK ABOUT YOUR BUDGET, SCHEDULE, AND WHAT YOUR CREATIVE VISION WILL BE.
(GFX:) calendar illuminates timeline	THEN YOU'LL CREATE A PRODUCTION TIMELINE . . . WITH DEADLINES FOR EACH TASK.
Video Clip: Producer & staff in meeting	MAKING A DOCUMENTARY BASICALLY BOILS DOWN TO THREE STAGES—FIRST, PRE-PRODUCTION, WHEN YOU ORGANIZE AND SET THINGS UP . . .

Graphic Effects

PHASE II: PRODUCTION

Be sure to keep track of everything you shoot on your Footage List.

ACTIVITY 9: WHATCHA SHOOTING?

CREATE A FOOTAGE LIST

MATERIALS NEEDED (1) VIDEO CAMERA AND EQUIPMENT, (2) *FOOTAGE LIST WORKSHEET* AND (3) PEN OR PENCIL

QUICK TAKE

So now that you have a rough script and some ideas as to the images you want to use, it's time to start shooting! A number of resources listed at the end of this study guide can help you in the logistics of shooting your documentary. One thing our producers want to be sure you do is to keep a list of everything you shoot in the form of a *Footage List* and be sure to *label your tapes* with at least a number and a date.

QUICK TIP

Remember that the National History Day (NHD) rules say *no extra people* in addition to yourself, your group, or the people you are interviewing, can appear in your documentary. So, if you do narration or create reenactments, only you and your group are allowed to do it!

TECH BYTE

Don't break the bank and buy a camera. You could borrow one from your school or even rent one from a video store.

TRY IT OUT!

- As you're shooting, use the Footage List Worksheet on the next page to keep track of your shots.

- Fill in the missing information at the top, and as you are filming, make a record for each new image that appears on camera on the numbered list. "TIME IN" means the start time that appears on your camcorder when you begin filming; "TIME OUT" means the end time when you stop.

- After you have completed your footage list, review your script and see if any of these new images can fit into your storyboard/script. Make a check mark on the Footage List Worksheet next to images you think might work, and update your script.

SOUND CHECK!

Be sure to monitor your sound when you are filming your interviewees. When you start filming, playback a little test to make sure you can hear the sound of your interview. When you're in post-production, make sure that your volume level is consistent throughout, taking extra care not to let music and sound effects overpower the voices of your narrator or the interviews.

(continued on next page)

ACTIVITY 9: WHATCHA SHOOTING? (cont.)

FOOTAGE LIST WORKSHEET

Be sure to use a new sheet for each tape.

TITLE OF PROJECT _____

TAPE # _____   DATE _____   PRODUCTION CREW _____

USE?	Write time code as it is on camera counter: Ex. (HH:MM:SS)—Hour, Minute, Seconds—(00:57:36) = 57 min. and 36 sec.
	1. Description: _____ Location: _____ Time In: _____ Time Out: _____ Camera Operator: _____ Interviewer: _____
	2. Description: _____ Location: _____ Time In: _____ Time Out: _____ Camera Operator: _____ Interviewer: _____
	3. Description: _____ Location: _____ Time In: _____ Time Out: _____ Camera Operator: _____ Interviewer: _____
	4. Description: _____ Location: _____ Time In: _____ Time Out: _____ Camera Operator: _____ Interviewer: _____
	5. Description: _____ Location: _____ Time In: _____ Time Out: _____ Camera Operator: _____ Interviewer: _____
	6. Description: _____ Location: _____ Time In: _____ Time Out: _____ Camera Operator: _____ Interviewer: _____
	7. Description: _____ Location: _____ Time In: _____ Time Out: _____ Camera Operator: _____ Interviewer: _____
	8. Description: _____ Location: _____ Time In: _____ Time Out: _____ Camera Operator: _____ Interviewer: _____
	9. Description: _____ Location: _____ Time In: _____ Time Out: _____ Camera Operator: _____ Interviewer: _____
	10. Description: _____ Location: _____ Time In: _____ Time Out: _____ Camera Operator: _____ Interviewer: _____

PHASE III: POST-PRODUCTION

Editing takes all the pieces you have recorded and turns them into a dynamic story.

ACTIVITY 10: WATCH IT!

MATERIALS NEEDED (1) TV AND CABLE ACCESS OR A VCR OR DVD TO WATCH A HISTORICAL DOCUMENTARY, AND (2) PEN AND PAPER

QUICK TAKE

Editing is where the magic really happens. You literally take all the pieces you have shot or recorded, and weave them into a dynamic story. To learn how to edit and to hone your editing skills, you can check out the resources we have included at the end of this guide or use the tutorials that come with any editing software program such as iMovie. Also, three good editing software programs to consider are the following

- Adobe® Premiere® Elements: http://www.adobe.com/products/premiereel/

- Apple's iMovie: http://www.apple.com/ilife/imovie/

- Apple's Final Cut Pro: http://www.apple.com/finalcutstudio/finalcutpro/

But, before you start editing, you have to know how a polished documentary looks, right? The best way to do that is to watch and study historical documentaries.

TRY IT OUT!

Select any The History Channel (THC) documentary and analyze it. For a list of programs, go to www.history.com. On a separate piece of paper, answer these questions.

- How is the documentary structured?

- Does the documentary have a major argument or goal? What would you say it is and how did the documentary express it?

- What kind of primary sources and secondary sources did the producers use? In what form (such as still photographs, footage, or interviews) did the sources appear?

- How could you find out from where the producers obtained these sources? From where did the producers get the footage for their film?

- How do you think the producers went about fact-checking their sources?

- What visually stood out to you in this documentary?

- How was sound or music used in the program?

- What were some strong elements of this documentary, and why? What were some weak elements, and why?

Compare and contrast your responses by selecting another documentary and answering the same questions.

ACTIVITY 11: WHERE CREDIT IS DUE

MATERIALS NEEDED (1) TV AND VCR OR DVD OR CABLE ACCESS TO WATCH DOCUMENTARIES, AND (2) TURABIAN OR MLA BIBLIOGRAPHY CITATION MANUAL

QUICK TAKE

You want to be sure you've properly given credit to the sources you have used in your documentary. For your National History Day (NHD) project, you have to do this in two different places and in two different ways.

The first place is in the *Credits*, which should appear on screen at the end of your documentary. *Your credits include every source that appears in your documentary, but not every source you consulted.* In general, your credits should have the following basic information: (1) list of major personnel who constructed the documentary (producer, editor, writer, narrator, performers, and so on); (2) list of interviewees' names if they appeared on camera; (3) list of archives or institutions used to obtain primary sources; (4) list of sources for any music used; (5) list of locations used for on-site filming; and (6) a brief Special Thanks list of people who were vital in the creation of your documentary. *A good rule of thumb with your credits is to make sure they are readable* (that is, choose a large enough type size and leave them on-screen long enough so that they can be read with ease.)

The second place you need to give credit where credit is due is in your *Annotated Bibliography, which includes every source you consulted that helped in the creation of your entire project.* Here, you want to follow either the Turabian or MLA format of citation and include in your annotation the specific parts of the source that you used in your documentary.

TRY IT OUT!

CREDITS

- Select any The History Channel (THC) documentary, watch it, and examine its credits closely. For a list of our programs go to www.history.com. Take notes on the information included in the credits, how they are organized, and their overall appearance.

- Check out the *Sample Credits* and the *Sample Credits Guide* on the following pages. *The Sample Credits* provide you with an example of credits a fictitious team might have at the end of its documentary, while the *Sample Credits Guide* explains what kind of information goes into your credits.

- Using the *Sample Credits* as a guide, type your credits on the computer. Remember that as you type your credits, you will have to make adjustments according to what is actually in your documentary. For example, if you interviewed an expert, but you didn't include her in your documentary, then you don't need to have an interview section list. Also, include the length of time you want the credits to appear on screen.

(continued on next page)

ANNOTATED BIBLIOGRAPHY

- Your first stop for understanding what should go in your annotated bibliography should be the NHD website www.nhd.org/AnnotatedBibliography.htm. Check out the FAQ under the National Contest link and the Rule Book for instructions on writing your bibliography.

- Check out the Sample Bibliography for specific examples of citing film footage and music credits in Turabian and MLA formats.

SAMPLE CREDITS (THE HISTORY CHANNEL SUGGESTED FORMAT)

ORDER OF CREDITS		LENGTH OF TIME ON SCREEN
A	**George Washington: The Triumph and Tragedy of Being a President With Wooden Teeth**	4 sec.
B	**Produced & Edited By** Priscilla Gomez Kwame Mensah Ali Muhammad Emily Pride	4 sec.
C	**Narrated By** Emily Pride	4 sec.
D	**Voice of George Washington** Kwame Mensah	
E	**Performers** Priscilla Gomez Kwame Mensah Ali Muhammad	
F	**Original Interviews Conducted With** Theodore Johnson, Ph.D. Julie Moore	6 sec.
G	**Other Interviews Appearing on Screen Taken From** Save Our History: George Washington's Workshop (The History Channel)	
H	**Filmed on Location** Fraunces Tavern Museum Historic Mount Vernon Mount Vernon Hotel & Museum	6 sec.
I	**Footage and Photos Provided By** Library of Congress New York Public Library Virginia Historical Society, Richmond, Virginia	
J	**Footage and Photos Taken From** Save Our History: George Washington's Workshop (The History Channel)	
K	**Music Taken From** Save Our History: George Washington's Workshop (The History Channel) The Patriot Original Motion Picture Score	
L	**Special Thanks** Joan Cooper Robert Gomez Cathy Pride	3 sec.

SAMPLE CREDITS GUIDE

A	**Title of Your Documentary**
B	**Produced & Edited** By List the names of all members on your team who created and edited your project. Note: *Everyone* should help in the production of your NHD project.
C	**Narrated By** If you use narration, list your name or the name(s) of any group member(s) who narrate(s) the documentary.
D	**Voice of George Washington** If you have any group members whose voices appear on camera and are not narrators, you should list their names. In this example, the team decided to have one member read excerpts from letters written by George Washington.
E	**Performers** If you have any group members who appear on screen, list their names as performers. In this example, the group decided to do reenactments.
F	**Original Interviews Conducted With** List the name(s) of any interviewees you personally filmed and who appeared in your documentary. If they have Ph.D.s, be sure to include their degree distinction after their names. This group conducted on-camera interviews with an expert and a curator of Mount Vernon.
G	**Other Interviews Appearing On Screen Taken From** If you use interviews from produced documentaries that you did not personally conduct, then under this heading, list the title of the documentary in italics and in parentheses indicate the producer.
H	**Filmed On Location** If you filmed on sites related to your topic, and incorporated that footage into your documentary, then list those sites under this heading. For example, this group was able to film at some of the actual historic sites where George Washington lived and worked.
I	**Footage and Photos Provided By** Under this heading, list the names of archives and institutions that provided primary sources that appear on screen. For example, this group found copyright-free photographs, paintings, and letters at these archives/institutions, and was able to scan the images for use in their documentary.
J	**Footage and Photos Taken From** If you use photographs, images, or any other material from produced documentaries, then under this heading list the documentary in italics and the producer in parentheses. In the example, the group obtained all of the other photographs and images that appear in their documentary from The History Channel's Save Our History: George Washington's Workshop.
K	**Music Taken From** If any music that appears in your documentary was not created by you or your team, then include the source from which you obtained it under this heading. List the title of the CD in italics and/or the title of the produced documentary in italics and the producer in parentheses. If you personally created the music for your documentary, then list your name(s) under the heading "Original Music Provided By."
L	**Special Thanks** List the important people and institutions who helped you in the creation of your documentary, and do not appear on screen. This list does not have to include everyone including the mail carrier who delivered your NHD registration materials. Rather, list people like your family members if they funded your project, or a teacher who spent every day after school working with you on your research, or an archivist who personally took you on a tour of all the primary sources in his institution related to your topic.

DON'T FORGET TO DOUBLE-CHECK YOUR SPELLING!

(continued on next page)

SAMPLE ANNOTATED BIBLIOGRAPHY

Citing Film Footage and Music in Turabian format

SECONDARY SOURCES

Footage

Save Our History: George Washington's Workshop. The History Channel, New York. 8:00 p.m., 17 February 2005.

This sixty-minute documentary provided us an overview of George Washington's estate, Mount Vernon. We obtained seventeen images of George Washington, Mount Vernon, and his letters from this documentary. We also used the interview of Richard Brookhiser, author of *Alexander Hamilton, American*, from this source.

Music

Williams, John. *The Patriot: Original Motion Picture Score*. 2000. Hollywood Records, 162258. Compact disc.

In addition to music from the *Save Our History: George Washington's Workshop* documentary, we used music from this movie score because it added dramatic effect. Although it is a modern-day creation, this source helped us understand contemporary ideas of what music from eighteenth-century America might have sounded like.

BIBLIOGRAPHY TIP

Be sure to follow NHD's instructions for citing primary sources. If you use footage from your primary sources, then mention that in your annotation of the source.

ACTIVITY 12: SCREEN IT!

MATERIALS NEEDED (1) TV WITH VCR OR DVD TO PLAY YOUR DOCUMENTARY, (2) COMFORTABLE VIEWING ROOM, (3) PEN AND PAPER TO TAKE NOTES, AND (4) POPCORN

QUICK TAKE

After you have completed a rough cut of your documentary, you can make sure your story makes sense by holding viewing parties with different "test audiences," such as your parents, teachers, neighbors, and friends. You may want to offer popcorn or other simple refreshments for your audiences.

TRY IT OUT!

- With your parents or guardian's permission, hold three different viewing parties, one for each of the following groups of people: (1) parents, (2) teachers or university professors, and (3) friends and neighbors.

- After showing your documentary, ask each group for objective, honest feedback. Allow them to speak openly without interruption and take notes as you ask them questions like these.

  - What was your first impression of the program?

  - What is the story?

  - What are some things that stood out to you in viewing the documentary?

  - Were there things that didn't make sense? What were they?

  - What do you think is the main argument (thesis) of the documentary?

  - Were there parts that seemed too slow? Too fast?

- Ask them if they have any questions, and practice responding like you'll have to do with NHD judges. Thank them at the end of the viewing party for their feedback.

- Look over your notes and consider which feedback can help you strengthen your documentary.

Remember You're not asking them to tell you whether or not they think your documentary is good, but you're trying to make sure that the story makes sense to "fresh eyes."

EXTENDED ACTIVITY: WHOSE RIGHT IS IT ANYWAY?

COPYRIGHT RIGHTS AND CLEARANCES

MATERIALS NEEDED (1) ONE OF YOUR PRIMARY SOURCES, (2) ACCESS TO THE INTERNET, AND (3) PEN OR PENCIL

QUICK TAKE

One of the most important issues in our line of work is copyright. *Copyright* is the law that protects the work of writers, filmmakers, and artists from being freely copied by other people. Many National History Day (NHD) students use produced documentaries to obtain primary images, sounds, and even musical soundtracks. For example, a student doing a project on the Civil Rights Movement might use footage of the March on Washington as it appears in the produced documentary *Eyes on the Prize* rather than contacting CBS News (the owner of the original footage). Another student doing a project on U.S. presidents may use an interview conducted with President Ronald Reagan he saw on a documentary without writing to and asking the original filmmaker for permission. Yet another student may use the soundtrack from the film *Windtalkers* in her project on Navajo code talkers. However, you must realize that *filmmakers should* never *copy footage, audio, or music from another produced work without obtaining consent* and *giving proper credit*. It is illegal to copy and the equivalent to plagiarizing another's work. Rather, to use primary source material that is copyrighted, filmmakers (1) go to the archive, (2) "OK" (permission) from the person or institution who owns that material, and (3) pay to use primary sources or copyrighted material in their documentary. Filmmakers keep themselves out of trouble by following these steps or by using material that is in the public domain (that is, copyright-free and available for anyone to use in any manner). Many sources created before 1923 are in public domain, as are some government materials. Using public domain images or audio means that although you wouldn't have to pay to use these sources or get permission, you do have to properly credit them in your credits and bibliography.

YOUR RESPONSIBILITIES IF YOU USE PRODUCED DOCUMENTARIES IN YOUR PROJECT

Because you are creating an *educational* documentary for the NHD competition and are following NHD's contest rules, your entry should fall within "fair use" copyright laws. But this means that

- Your documentary can only be shown within NHD competitions.

- You must have *proper credits* in your film.

- You must list and credit *all* of your sources in your annotated bibliography.

- You cannot take and use verbatim the narration of another documentary.

If you have any questions regarding copyright issues, you should contact the NHD office or an attorney directly. In preparing your entry for NHD, you, your teacher, and your parents or guardians should be mindful of copyright issues. A helpful source to consult with respect to these issues is The Copyright Kids webpage, operated by The Copyright Society of the U.S.A. This page can be found at http://www.copyrightkids.org/.

(continued on next page)

TRY IT OUT!

- To get a sense of how the professionals obtain copyright clearance, read through the following *Five Key Steps Filmmakers Take* (to obtain permission to use copyrighted materials).

- Afterward, choose a primary source you have found and complete the *Primary Source Licensing Worksheet* on the next page.

FIVE KEY STEPS FILMMAKERS TAKE*
(TO OBTAIN PERMISSION TO USE COPYRIGHTED MATERIALS)

1. **Find out** which archive holds the primary sources related to the topic.

2. **Select** the key primary sources necessary for the documentary.

3. **Obtain a license** for the use of each image and recording by identifying who owns copyright and obtaining their permission to use it in the documentary. If it is a book, look at the publication information and contact the publisher. If it is a photograph, look on the back and see if there's any information written there. If it is a video, look at the credits. Write a letter directly to the owner and explain how, why, and for how long you want to use the material in their documentary. The copyright owner then writes back with an official "OK" Sometimes, the copyright owner may require a fee for the use of the material and may put restrictions on how the material can be used.

4. With a letter in writing from the copyright owner giving consent, *complete an application* with the archive or institution that has the primary source. Include a copy of the consent letter along with payment if required by the archive or institution for use of the primary source.

5. The archive or institution will in turn give a reproduction or reprint of the primary source for use in the documentary.

This is a rough overview of the key steps filmmakers take when finding and using primary sources. There are some hidden steps along the way, but the result is that the filmmaker would have legally obtained the right to use the copyrighted material and therefore, avoid breaking any laws.

PRIMARY SOURCE LICENSING WORKSHEET

Working with one of the primary sources (photograph, painting, video, or audio) you found during your research, fill in the missing information below. You may have to play detective to find what you're looking for, but you'll be one step closer to doing it like the pros! Check out the resources at the end of this guide for more help.

Your Name _____

Title of Source (if available) _____

Type of Source (Place a check mark)

____ Moving Image   ____ Still Image   ____ Audio Recording

Brief Description of this Source (for example, "Image of Geronimo at the 1901 Pan-American Exposition")

_____

_____

Repository/Library/Archive where this source can be found _____

Who officially owns the copyright to this image? _____

Where/how did you find this information? _____

How could you find out how much it would cost to obtain the rights to use this source?

_____

If you are able to, how much would it cost to obtain the rights to use this source in your documentary?

_____

Length of time this image is used in your documentary _____

FINAL WORDS

That's it. Those are the top twelve activities we think will strengthen your skills as a filmmaker of historical documentaries. We hope that you have found *How to Create a Historical Documentary* and this study guide helpful in your project. Be sure to check out the resources in the next section for more in-depth, step-by-step strategies.

If there are only three things that you take away from our DVD and guide, we hope they are these:

1. The most important step in creating your documentary is research.

2. *Don't spend a lot of money!* Borrow resources and focus on telling a dynamite story.

3. The best free resource you'll need in making your documentary is a passion to tell the story you've discovered.

If you keep these three pointers in mind, your historical documentary for the National History Day competition will have already won the best prize ever.

Good luck on your project!

The History Channel

PART V: RESOURCES

The History Channel website: www.history.com

National History Day website: www.nhd.org

TOP FIVE STEP-BY-STEP RESOURCES

1. *The Past In Pixels: Using iMovie to Create an NHD Documentary* **(DVD)** Available only from the NHD, this program takes you through the step-by-step process of creating a documentary using Apple's iMovie program. It provides examples and has students explain how they have used the program, and it is wonderful for both students and teachers. To order a copy, go to the NHD website: www.nhd.org.

2. *Adobe Digital Kids Club.* http://www.adobe.com/education/digkids/main.html A superb website that takes you through the shooting and editing processes, and includes lesson plans for educators.

3. **"Video Guide."** *Challenge 2000. Project-Based Learning with Multimedia.* http://pblmm.k12.ca.us/TechHelp/VideoHelp/VideoGuide.html A step-by-step guide with key activities to better learn the production and post-production processes.

4. **Rabiger, Michael.** *Directing the Documentary,* 3rd ed. Boston: Focal Press, 1998. This book contains excellent worksheets and solid detailed steps on creating a documentary film. "Chapter 14: Interviewing" and pages 235–236 offer tips about what to do before, during, and after the interview. "Surviving Your Critics and Making Use of What They Say" (pages 291–292) offers some helpful hints for obtaining feedback from your viewing audiences.

5. Rosenthal, Alan. *Writing, Directing, and Producing Documentary Films and Videos,* Rev. ed. Carbondale: Southern Illinois University Press, 1996. This is a staple book in many college-level documentary filmmaking courses today. It offers a detailed take on all aspects of creating your documentary. See a sample synopsis on pages 123–124. Also, check out Rosenthal's chapter, "The History Documentary," for an interesting take on what the historical documentary is (pages 297–306).

RESOURCES REFERENCED IN THE ACTIVITIES

1. National History Day Contest Rule Book: http://www.nhd.org/Rules.htm

2. *Worksheet Creating A Project:* http://www.nhd.org/CreatingaProject.htm

3. *Working in Groups* contract and questionnaire: http://www.nhd.org/CreatingaProject.htm

4. *Topic selection worksheet:* http://www.nhd.org/CreatingaProject.htm

5. A Research Roadmap: http://www.nhd.org/ResearchRoadmap.htm

6. Research strategy worksheet: http://www.nhd.org/CreatingaProject.htm

7. "Oral History Guidelines—Study Guide." *The History Channel Classroom:* http://www.historychannel.com/classroom/oralhistguidelines.pdf

8. *Video Storyboard Form:* http://www.nhd.org/Documentary.htm

ADDITIONAL RESOURCES

Copyright—Rights and Clearances

BOOKS

Stim, Richard. *Getting Permission: How to License and Clear Copyrighted Materials Online & Off.* Consolidated Printers, 2000.

WEBSITES

Association for Information Media and Equipment: http://www.aime.org/

Copyright Kids: http://www.copyrightkids.org

Fair Use Guidelines for Educational Multimedia: http://www.utsystem.edu/ogc/intellectualproperty/ccmcguid.htm

Stanford University Libraries: Copyright & Fair Use: http://fairuse.stanford.edu/index.html

Media Literacy

Action Coalition for Media Education: http://www.acmecoalition.org

Alliance for a Media Literate America: http://www.amlainfo.org

Cable in the Classroom: http://www.ciconline.com

Center for Media Literacy: http://www.medialit.org

Documentary Filmmaking

Apple iLife in the Classroom: http://www.apple.com/education/ilife/ A great website if you're using iMovie or other Apple products.

Turn Your Students into Documentary Filmmakers: http://www.apple.com/education/documentary/ Site for educators.

DV Café. http://www.dvshop.ca/dvcafe.html A comprehensive website on all things related to digital filmmaking. If you are just starting out, go to their "Beginners DV" section.

Youth Media Distribution: http://www.ymdi.org/* A comprehensive website for young filmmakers that features:

- Step-by-step plans for production, resources, and information on copyright

- Lesson plans for educators: http://www.ymdi.org/instructors/

*Note this website emphasizes distributing your documentary, but if you have created your entry for National History Day and it contains copyrighted material for which you did not get permission, then *you should not show your documentary to an outside public.*

REFERENCES

1. Jim Schmidt, Writing Historical Essays: An Introduction" http://www3.niu.edu/history/manual.htm

2. This list is based on Document Analysis Worksheets created by the National Archives and Records Administration's education staff: http://www.archives.gov/education/lessons/index.html and on Kathryn Walbert, "Reading Primary Sources: An Introduction for Students," http://www.learnnc.org/students/9-12/research/print/readingprimaryintro

3. Stacey Bredhoff, *American Originals* (Washington, DC: National Archives and Records Administration in association with the University of Washington Press), 2001, 6.

ABOUT THE AUTHOR

Amma Ghartey-Tagoe is a former NHD national contest participant, winning 1st Place, Senior Individual Performance in 1996. As an intern for The History Channel, Amma worked under Dr. Libby O'Connell on the creation of educational materials for The History Channel and authored several study guides for on-air programming, including Voices of Civil Rights.

Amma earned a degree in Afro-American Studies with a focus on history from Harvard University. Amma is currently a graduate student at New York University-Titsh School of the Arts, working on a doctorate in performance studies, a research and practical study of the intersections of theater, film, television and history.

ACKNOWLEDGMENTS

FOR THE HISTORY CHANNEL

PRESIDENT & CHIEF EXECUTIVE OFFICER
Abbe Raven

EXECUTIVE EDITOR
Libby H. O'Connell, Ph.D.

WRITER
Amma Y. Ghartey-Tagoe

CONTENT ADVISORS
Virginia E. Kuppek
Nuchada Ruchira

COPY EDITOR
Kimberly Gilmore, Ph.D.

BUSINESS MANAGER
Mead Rust

BUSINESS COORDINATOR
Lissette Fong-Belliard

FOR NATIONAL HISTORY DAY

EXECUTIVE EDITOR
Cathy Gorn, Ph.D.

DVD CREDITS

EXECUTIVE PRODUCER
Libby H. O'Connell, Ph.D.

PRODUCED & WRITTEN BY
Barbra Dannov
Nuchada Ruchira

ASSOCIATE PRODUCER
Amma Y. Ghartey-Tagoe

NARRATOR
Pat Kiernan

ADDITIONAL RESEARCH
Monique Frumberg
Jeff Mandell

INTERVIEWEES
Libby H. O'Connell, Ph.D.
David Fannon
Monique Frumberg

ACTORS
Elizabeth Kelly
THC Production Staff

NHD wishes to thank the sponsors of How to Create a Historical Documentary:

NOTES

NOTES

NOTES